CW00859114

The Deadman Tape

Paul Deadman plays and replays the eight tapes he has found in the attic of his new home, and longs to know more about them. Did the boy who told the story of how his gentle, loving father was suddenly deported as an illegal immigrant, know, for example, the girl whose wild breaking-and-entering escapade ended in unintentional tragedy? Did the girl whose adored father proved such a let-down know the boy who couldn't decide how to ask a girl out? Where are all these young people now, who told their stories so vividly on discarded tapes?

The Deadman Tapes

Michael Rosen

ANDRE DEUTSCH

First Published in 1989 by
André Deutsch Limited
105–106 Great Russell Street, London WC1B 3LJ

British Library Cataloguing in Publication Data

Rosen, Michael, *1954–*
  The Deadman Tapes.
  I. Title
  823′.914[F]

  ISBN 0 233 98465 8

Printed in Great Britain by
Ebenezer Baylis and Son Limited, Worcester

To the Institute of Youth and Community Affairs

Dear sir or madam,

Recently my parents and I moved house and while going through the attic in my present house, I came across a box of tapes. None of them were marked so I had no idea who made them, or for what purpose. Similarly, I have no idea who the speakers are. As a guess, I would think they are part of some investigation or other but I can't think of the exact nature of it. On the other hand they might be part of some work someone was doing in connection with an artistic enterprise, like a play or a novel perhaps. I have tried to talk to the previous occupiers of the house about the material but they claim complete ignorance of the matter. The whole thing is a mystery. I have no use for the tapes but thought they might be of some interest to someone at your Institute.

Yours

Paul Deadman

Institute of Community Affairs

Dear Mr Paul Deadman,

Thank you for sending us the tapes. We have played several of them and we are agreed here that they are of no use to us whatsoever. We have a policy of only using material made by staff or students.

Yours sincerely,

Marghanita Wilmslow (Dr)

enc: 8 tapes, unmarked

To the Gazette

Dear Editor,

When our family moved into a new house, I came across a box of tapes in the attic. The box was marked: 'Research interviews' but each tape was unmarked. I have contacted the previous occupiers of the house – they deny all knowledge of it. Rather than throw them away, my first inclination was to send them to you as they are of local interest. Perhaps they would be suitable for printing extracts from them in your paper.

Yours

P. Deadman

Dear Paul,

Thanks for your letter and tapes. What an interesting little number! I found them quite entertaining but to be honest we can't touch this sort of thing at all. For starters, we've got no way of proving that they are authentic. Someone could easily have made them up. Secondly we would get ourselves into all kinds of difficulty with the moral crusaders who would say we were peddling immoral rubbish etc etc.

Anyway, thanks for sending them to us; I return them to you in a separate parcel.

    Best of luck

    Ron Tinsley
    Editor

No one wants to read these. Am I the only one who's interested? Why do I sit and listen to them over and over again trying to get a picture of who is talking? The other night I went to sleep with one of the tapes playing. I woke up and it was still playing and I thought he was in the room. Half-asleep I started talking to him. I know them all now. I know these people I've never met.

This first tape sounds like it's a guy about the same age as me. He speaks slowly and steadily – like he's never told any of it before. There's someone else in the room listening to him. It's a woman and she coughs.

The last time I saw him
was about seven years ago when I was eight.
He had to go back.
The police knew he was here illegally,
he had never married my mum
so he didn't have a leg to stand on.
They just put him on a boat
and he was gone.
One moment I had a dad
and the next
he had been taken off.
It felt like he had been kidnapped.
They just said he was breaking the law by being here.
He wasn't breaking the law
in any other way,
he was working on sites,
building sites.

We all wrote to him
but we never heard a thing.
He just disappeared off the face of the earth.
He had no right to do that. It left a great big hole.

I don't know what Mum thought:
she never said.
She never spoke about it.
We used to see her from time to time
sitting there looking sad,
but we never dared say anything

6

and she never said anything to us about it.
We just knew it was something we couldn't speak about.

Just every so often
she'd sit us down
and say,
'Write to your dad.'
I never knew what to say
and the longer it went that we had never seen him
or heard from him
the harder it was to think of anything to say.
I just used to write
things like
'I'm getting on all right at school'
even when I wasn't.

We had a few photos of him.
One of them was taken with all of us crowding into a
    little booth
and we're all waving and pulling mad faces
and he looks really mad,
peeping over the top of my head
with the baby on his knee.
He looks so much part of the family,
he looks so much that he belongs there
that when I came to look away from the photo
I could never figure out
why he wasn't with us now.
There was another one of him in the park
with his foot on a football.
I remember when that was taken.
We had gone over the park, just him and me,
and played football
and Mum had come along later
and she had this new camera
so she said she wanted to take a picture of him.
And he's standing there like he's
just won the world cup or something,

hands folded across his chest.
He was good at football.
I liked that, when we used to go over the park
and play together
and he used to shout things in his language:
it was funny.

He brought his mum over once.
She was ancient.
All her hands were knobbly and wrinkled
and he was so pleased she'd come to see us.
He kept putting his hand on my head
and standing next to me for her to look at us
and she kept nodding and chewing her lips
and smiling in her eyes.
He cried when she went back.
He cried buckets.
He put his head on his arms
on the table and just cried and cried.
It was scarey –
he was so big and strong
and here he was helpless
because his Mum had gone home.
I felt more grown up than he was
for a moment.
and that IS scarey
because you know inside
you are not very grown up at all.

It was great when he did the cooking
He used to stand at the cooker
throwing things in the pan
and shouting.
He wasn't cross
it was just that he liked to shout about it.
And he used to sing these loud songs
in his language.
When we asked him what they meant

he'd burst out laughing
and say our ears were too young.

He was terrible when he was cross
he used to fling his arms about,
and say that his life wasn't worth living,
a man's life is a dog's life
and he'd swear like mad
which was actually quite funny
because he would get all the swear words wrong.
He never said bloody.
It was always
blooding.
What am I?
Just a blooding slave, am I?
Blooding hell!
But you couldn't laugh.
That was one thing he couldn't stand.
If he thought you were laughing at him
he blew a fuse:
Those blooding kids!

He could make things with a penknife.
He used to get hold of bits of wood
and make little men
and cars and things
and they were brilliant
and then he'd line them up on the table and make up
    stories
about them.
There was the man who never died –
no matter what happened to him
he never died.
He was in crashes
he used to dive off the edge of cliffs
(which was the table)
and he'd lie there for days
but he got himself together

and crawled to a river and floated down river
and found help.
He was in fires,
he was in a house when it was bombed,
but he always escaped
because he would live for ever.
We called him Forever Man
and we'd say,
'Tell us another one about Forever Man,'
and he would.

And sometimes he would tell us stories
he said that his mother had told him.
One of them used to scare me like hell
but I always got him to tell it to me again and again.

There was this man
and he had to go to war
and so his lady and his son were left alone.
When the boy went to school
the boy saw his mother
with some other men,
and so the boy says,
'When daddy comes I'm going to tell him
what I've seen with my own eyes.'
So then the lady kills the little boy.
When the man comes home
he says,
'Where's my son?'
And the woman says,
'He's down at his gran's.'
So the man takes his horse
and goes down to his mother's house.
When he gets there he goes,
'Where's the boy?'
and the gran says,
'It's three years since I've seen him
three years since I've kissed him.'

So he goes back to his wife and says,
'Where's the boy?
He's not down at his gran's.'
So she says,
'He's down at his godmother's.'
So the man gets on his horse
and he goes down to the godmother's
and he says,
'Where's my boy?'
And she says,
'It's three months since I've seen him
In three months I've forgotten him.'
So he goes back to his lady
and he says,
'Where is my son?
he's not at his gran's
and he's not at his godmother's.'
So she says,
'He's at school.'
So he gets on the horse
and he gets to the school.
When he gets there
he says to the teacher,
'Where's my son?'
'It's three days since I've seen him
it's three days, so I've expelled him.'
So he goes back to his wife again
and she says,
'Just sit down and eat your dinner
and then you can go out looking for him.'
And the woman has cooked the boys heart and lungs
to poison the man.
He's just about to cut the first piece
when the voice box
calls out to him and says,
'If you're my dad
kneel down and kiss me.

If not
you kill me.'
So the man took the woman out and killed her.

It was terrifying, the way
he used to tell us that one.
When the voice box speaks up out of his dinner
I used to come over all creepy
I used to get prickles all down my neck.

He used to go out to meetings.
I went with him once
the room was full of men shouting.
I didn't like it much
but sometimes we went on marches
and that was better.
I got to hold the banner
then when the men shouted
the noise of it filled the street.
He used to say,
'One day there will no thieves
and no soldiers.
No thieves, no soldiers,
because everyone will have enough
so no one will need to want what someone else has got.'
He used to say,
'We have to stick together.'
And he'd get this box of matches out,
because if you take one match
you can break it.
If you take two matches
you can break them.
If you take three matches you can break them,
but if you take the whole box of matches
you can't break them.
That's why we stick together –
if we all stick together

they can't break us.
Then all of a sudden he was gone.

It was hard for Mum,
she had something wrong with her
so she couldn't do a proper job.
We just had to live
on what she got from the post office
after he left.
She said
that it didn't make us worse than anybody else
just because we had to live like that.
She said
her mother
and her mother before that
and her mother before that
had all worked from the age of twelve
till the day they dropped,
so it was only fair that someone in the family
got a bit.
'After all,'
she'd say,
'If I had been a born lord or lady
I'd've got what my mother or father had left me.'
And everything any lord or lady had
was through the likes of her mother
working for them.
So whenever she got back from the post office
she'd say,
'I've got my inherited wealth in here,'
and then she'd laugh.

She never had a boy friend.
I think some tried it.
There were various blokes who used to call round
but they never stayed long.
They might stay to tea
but no later,

they were always gone before our bedtime.
It was like she didn't want to risk them
being about with her on her own.
They were always out the door.
That was all six or seven years ago.

I got to thinking I'd never see him again
but suddenly one day
he's there again.
He's at the door
no letter
no warning
nothing
and he's there.

It felt so strange.
Mum and him cried loads,
and she dashed about all over the place.
I felt really clumsy and big.
The last time I'd seen him
he could pick me up and throw me about
now I was tall as he was.
My arms felt too long and I wanted to sit down
but he made me stand up
and he slapped me on the shoulder.
His English was terrible.
He could scarcely say a word
but it didn't matter much.

He got a job on the sites again.

About two weeks after he got back
one evening we were
called out.
He was killed on the site.
It was a huge insurance place they were finishing off
with a high hall big enough for trees in it.
He'd been on a scaffold tower
making good after the electrician

and the tower started falling away under his feet.
He just had time to grab a chain for a light fitting
and he hung there yelling for help
but it couldn't take his weight
and he broke his neck.

The firm was to blame,
they were using a broken scaffold tower.
We should have got thousands of pounds for it
in compensation
but the judge said
we couldn't prove we were anything to do with him
and he was an illegal immigrant anyway.

My uncle said
they saved money by not getting a new tower
they saved money by not paying Dad's stamps
they saved money by not paying his compensation.
You want to get rich?
Now you know how.

The firm sent Mum a letter
saying how sorry they were
but it was more than she could take.
Overall
looking back at all those years
she lost out all round really.
I didn't
but she did.

I'm left thinking about ordinariness. I am ordinary. I don't
know anyone else who is ordinary as I am. Everything that
has happened to me is ordinary. I am a stack of ordinariness.
That doesn't mean I haven't got hope.

People who don't hope:
dossers
bag women
alcoholics
druggies
suicides
I think everyone is allowed to hope for enough space to live in, enough time for yourself and enough food. But not everyone gets these things, do they?

This sounds like she was seventeen when she spoke this. Quite posh, I think she's holding the microphone and talking into it because it pops sometimes. She's someone I would stare at. What's new? Who *don't* I stare at?

I loved my dad
his hands were always cold,
and right from the time I was very young
I used to keep them warm
by trying to cover them up with my hands.
I used to say my hands were his gloves.

At the weekends
he used to wear a pair of grey corduroy trousers
that were soft and baggy
and a sweater that had been boiled
so it was all felted and furry.

I didn't see much of him during the week,
evenings were with Mum.
I never really knew what his job was.
It was something medical,
but he wasn't a doctor
though he *had been* a doctor
and it meant that he was always out.
He had to do talks.

He had to go away as well.
He went all over the world
looking at hospitals and doctors.
He went to India and Hong Kong
and Nigeria and loads of places.
His coming back was amazing.
Just to think of it

is enough to make me clench my hands
with the excitement of it.
I always knew the exact time of his flight
and I used to work out
exactly how long it'd take him
to get from the airport to home.

And the presents –
there was the poster of a harbour,
I think it was Hong Kong,
and there were thousands and thousands of boats
and every boat was full of people.
I'd lie in bed
and think of all those thousands of people
who I didn't know and they didn't know that
I had this picture of them and their boats.
I could never believe that they were real.

There was a tin train set.
It was clockwork
and all I had was enough rails to make a circle
and the train went clanking
round and round the circle.
It was green and silver
and if you pressed the carriages too hard
they dented.

The house was full of his presents.
There were plates on the wall
and jugs and mats and little statues
on the window sill in the bathroom
and strange bits of straw or bark or glass
that he'd picked up in some city
on the other side of the world.

I imagined him doing it:
walking through markets in the blazing sun
or along crowded streets
and he was carefully choosing things –

this thing? no, that thing . . .
no, she's a bit too young for that . . .
ah, just right.
And he was thinking about me
and the lovely things he was going to bring back for me.

I didn't *know* my mother.
She wasn't a person,
she was a nuisance,
a kind of load on your back.
A day or an evening with her,
I used to think, was made up of bricks,
very boring bricks.
So there was the washing-up brick.
She always got to the sink
before the end of the meal
and the moment she got there
she complained that she was the one
that had to do the washing up.

Then there was my hair.
I used to see each new subject coming up
as this 'brick'
that she was building her time with.

The hair brick
was always about how it was OK to have long hair
if you kept it clean.
So why not have short hair
because you didn't have to wash it so often?

And there were hundreds of other bricks,
like putting the Radio Times back under the telly;
changing the toilet roll if you finished one;
eating apple cores because they were good for you;
remembering to pour away the washing up water;
putting the tomatoes on the top of the shopping bag
otherwise they came back squashed . . .
oh, and loads more.

Sometimes whole evenings
were made out of these bricks
and I'd sit there
and it was like background music
to my dreams of Dad in a rickshaw
being pulled through the streets
or gliding across America in the Santa Fe Express
with windows in the roof of the carriages
so you could see the Rocky Mountains
and the bison on the plains . . .

I never knew why my mum was the most boring person
    in the world,
and if anyone had ever asked me
I'd've said it was her fault.
If anyone had said
she's boring because she's got nothing to do
but wait for your dad to come home,
I'd've said I didn't care.

And I never thought about what my dad did.
I knew it was important, because he was my dad.
But if someone had said
he's just a big 'I-am',
who goes all round the world
to tell people how important he is,
how important English people are,
how English people pretend to know about everything –
especially about getting people in other countries
to buy things they don't need,
to borrow money they can't afford to pay back
and grow things they can't eat.
If someone had said all that then
I'd've cried.
I'd've said,
'No no no he's wonderful.'

And if someone had said
he was just a selfish sod

who led this life swanning round the world
while his family was stuck at home waiting,
and the moment he got back
it was there ready to feed his face
and warm his slippers,
I'd've said he deserved it,
because he was so clever and nice.

And if someone had said
he was probably knocking off his personal assistant
who used to go on all these trips with him,
then I'd've said good luck to him
because he was clever
and good looking
and any nice bloke like him
would have got fed up with my mum years ago.

That's what I'd've said,
if anyone had said any of those things to me,
but they didn't
not a breath of it
and all the time I thought it was Wonderful Dad
and Dreary Dreary Mum.

Then something changed everything.

I knew that some of the things he did
were sort of secret.
It wasn't that they were dangerous
but that no one was really supposed to know.
He'd change the subject sometimes
when you asked him where he was going.
There was a cupboard with drawers
that was always locked,
and Mum used to have a serious face
that she'd put on, as if to say
'Important',
as he was going out of the house.

So all this went on for years,
till I was sixteen, in fact.

Now I'm a nosey parker,
very, very nosey
and I got curious about Dad's work.
I wanted to know what he did
and where he went
and why he went there.
I used to read the things on his desk.

Some of it was really amazing.
There were reports on epidemics of typhoid in Uganda
and how hundreds and hundreds of people died in one
    week.
There was a horrible thing about leprosy
how there's loads of it about
and it's getting worse,
it's spreading towards this country
and they don't know how you get it.
Rabies – with people dying because they hate water,
and of course AIDS, AIDS, AIDS.

Then one day I found it.
It looked like all the other things on the desk.
There was nothing on it
that said it was different.
It wasn't printed,
it was like a photocopy of something that had been
    typed.
It was lying under something from the United Nations.

It was about what his job would be
if there was a nuclear war.

I didn't even know he had a job planned
for after the nuclear war.

As far as I could work out
he had to supervise all the doctors.
He had to tell them where to go
after the bomb.
He had a special place
where he had to go to do it,
and we wouldn't be there.

Actually I didn't really get that far
to find out.

You see I picked it up
and I was reading it
and Mum was there in the room behind me.
I didn't know she'd come in.
She said, what was I reading
and I said, this,
and I gave it to her
in a sort of sneering way
as if to say,
I bet you don't understand it,
and look at me, naughty clever me,
I know more about Dad than you do.

So then she started reading it
and I watched her face
and her eyes went dark and panicky
and she didn't look stupid or tiresome or boring
any more.
She was someone who was scared.

So I said,
'What is it?
What does it say?'
and she wouldn't tell me.
So I got cross
and I said she had to tell me
because I was the one who found it

and she wouldn't know what was in it
if I hadn't told her.

Then she started crying
and said she couldn't tell me.
So I said, 'Is it because it's secret?'
And she said 'No,'
So I said, 'Why then?'
And she said that there were so many things I didn't
    understand.
Now, I hate that, when people say things like that to me.
So I said, 'Like what?'

Then she said,
'Like what it means to be hit.'
I had no idea what she was talking about
and I said so.
She then had this whole outburst
about how, as far I was concerned
Dad could do no wrong
and it has always been like that.
How she could never get near me,
how all I ever thought about was him,
how I used to look through her
even when I was little,
how I didn't know the way he treated her.

Did I know, for example, that he beat her once?
She had said that his mother spoiled him
and he'd gone into a frenzy
and beaten her
so she had to pretend to be ill
until the bruises went away.

Did I know that he made her promise that
she'd never get a job,
it would look bad if she did,
as if they needed the money
or as if home life wasn't good enough for her.

And she'd agreed
because there did seem so much to do
around the house.
To keep it how he liked it.

Did I know about
how she wasn't able to go and see her brother
when he was dying
because dad was going away on a trip.
All she'd asked him for, was a day's postponement
so she could have been at her brother's bedside.
Dad had said it was typical of her
to put something in the way of his career
just as he was on the brink of something important.

Oh, she said,
'I could tell you so much
but you wouldn't listen.'

So then I said,
'Well, why don't you tell me
what's in the report?
What does it say?'

So then she said,
'All right, I will tell you.
It says
he is responsible for Public Health
if a nuclear attack comes.
He's in charge of medical care,
and that means he sits in a government shelter
that they've made.
It's sitting there now,
and it's got phones and radios and televisions
and food and beds . . .
. . . and he's got a place there.

We don't have a place there.

This is for essential personnel only.
But more than that,' she said,
'Your darling father has to promise
that he will not try to get his family in there
when the bomb drops.
He won't try to smuggle them in.
He has to understand that
it may be necessary to shoot looters and intruders,
that is, anyone who thinks
they ought to be in there
with him . . .
That could be me
or it could be you.
The whole thing is too fantastic.'
And then she broke down again.

'The whole thing is mad,' she said.

So I said, 'I thought no one was going to live
after the bomb, anyway.'
And she says,
'Of course not, I know that
but the point is what's going through his mind now?
He's made himself ready to do these things,
to us.
I don't know who makes these plans
but it seems as if they actually think someone's going to
    win
a nuclear war.
I know someone who isn't going to win,
that's you and me.'
I listened to the whole thing
and it seemed like I was being sentenced to death;
awful horrible feeling all over,
just amazed that this stupid mother of mine
was talking as if she was in control,
as if she knew what she was talking about
and it wasn't the hoovering or something.

26

You see, I should have explained,
that though I thought she was stupid, over the years
there was a bit of me that couldn't understand
something about her.
I knew she'd been to college –
she was going to be a doctor as well, I think,
but it all got broken off.
I never found out why exactly
until much later on.

Basically it was because she got pregnant with Dad
before they got married,
and she had the baby
and it was me.

Anyway,
there we were
alone with this horrible report.
We made some tea
And we walked about,
we looked out of the window,
we pretended we hadn't seen it,
and then she said,
'I'll have to leave him.
I could have done it a hundred times before
when I knew about his women,
when he extended his trips,
when he didn't come home,
when he hit me that time,
but there was you.'
She said,
'I stayed for you,
and all this time,
you couldn't have cared less.
If I'd've said, anytime in the last sixteen years,
that I was leaving,
you'd've said, "Goody, goody".'

She was right,
I would have done.
So I said,
'Where are you going?'
And she said
She'd go to her sister's.
And I just said,
'Can I come?'
And I did.
We did.
We left.
We told him why.
Mum wrote everything down
and sent it to him.

I promise I will never describe myself as 'reasonable'. The trouble is this girl thought that her dad was reasonable. I will think of myself as grown-up the moment I stop trying to be reasonable. Are reasonable people dangerous?

This boy says he's sixteen. He's a space case, talks slowly –
not because he's thinking what he's saying but like he
doesn't feel anything. The recording sounds like it was made
down a sewer. Maybe he's a cabbage.

My mum and dad split up.
No big deal.

I was ten at the time.
I can't say as I saw it coming
but then it wasn't a shock either.
I just kind of thought;
Oh yeah, you're splitting up, are you?
Can I have some more chips, please.
Maybe I thought they were never that keen on each
    other.
But then you don't expect your mum and dad to be
all over each other, do you?
I mean how many kids walk into a room
and see their mums and dads groping on the sofa?
They don't seem to need to, do they?
Well, mine didn't anyway.
Anyhow, one day I got in from school
and they were both there
all over the place
ranting and crying and yelling.
And then I got the:
'You tell him'.
'No, you tell him'
business.
I just stood there looking at them:
'You tell him.'
'No, you tell him.'

I didn't have a clue what they were talking about.
Mum told me.
'We're splitting up,' she says.
Then they spent the next half an hour looking at me.
They kept walking round and round the place
glancing at me.
I thought. 'What have I done wrong?
What do they keep looking at me for?
I haven't nicked anything, have I?
There was a strawberry cheese cake in the fridge,
I knew it was left over from the day before
and I kept thinking about it,
so I said,
'Can I have some of that cake?'
and Dad went bananas.
He starts saying that I'm crazy
and it's all Mum's fault.
'Look at him,' he says,
'Look at him.
He's got no go in him
he walks about with his eyes shut
and the rest of the time sits there daydreaming.
Don't ask him what he's daydreaming about
he always says
I don't know
I don't know
I don't know.'
Then he starts shouting at Mum,
saying it's her fault I'm like that.
Mum started going on about the toilet.
She was saying how he had never fixed the cistern,
so you couldn't flush the chain properly
and here we were in the twentieth century
and we were living like cave men
all because dad couldn't lift a finger.
Anyway, he left.
The next few weeks didn't seem much different.

Dad wasn't there watching the telly
and complaining about the spuds not being cooked
    properly.
Mum started seeing a lot of her friend Sue.
They were at it yakking away in the kitchen all night.
I sat and watched telly or read magazines and stuff.
Sometimes I played computer games for hours and hours
and I could hear them in the kitchen.

Dad used to call for me on Sunday mornings.
He never said where he was living
but sometimes we went up his mother's
my nan's.
Now I think of it
we nearly always went up Nan's
and he sat there watching the telly.
Sometimes we went to the chip shop
and once we went over to his mate, Jeff's, house
and I played with his little kid, Jason.

Anyway,
back at home,
after about four or five weeks
this Sue suddenly stops coming round
And Mum started spending hours and hours
staring at the wall.
That didn't seem to make much difference either.
I went on playing computer games, except now
instead of hearing her and Sue going at it
talk talk talk
from the other room
there was just Mum staring at the wall.
Then when Sunday came
she says,
'Your dad won't be over today, right?'
I said, 'OK.'
I played out for the rest of the day
with the kids in the street.

That night at tea time she says,
'Dad's gone to live with Sue.'
So I said,
'Do I go over their place now?'
'No you don't,' she says.
'OK,' I said.

I knew Sue's place quite well.
She had two kids,
a girl about my age and a boy a bit younger,
and she was married to a bloke called Ron
who was a gardener,
doing up other people's gardens.
I quite liked it over there.
Sue made brilliant hamburgers.
Their place wasn't very big
and I remember wondering where Dad's room was.
I didn't wonder very long.
I didn't see Dad for a few weeks.
One night Mum said,
'Do you miss your Dad?'
I said, 'Not much.'
So she said,
'If it was me that had gone
would you miss me?'
And I said,
'I don't know.'
'Ron is furious,' she said.
I said, 'It must be pretty crowded there now.'
Mum said,
'Your Dad doesn't take up more space than Ron,
does he?'

There was a long silence.

A few weeks after this Mum says,
'From now on,

you go to see your Dad
every weekend
Saturday morning to Sunday evening.'
I said,
'OK.'
To start off
It was all right
over there, though
Sue's boy hated me
and her girl didn't want to play much.
I had to sleep in the boy's bedroom.
He collected old football programmes
and I used to sit on the bed looking through them.
But then one day
Sue says I wasn't allowed to look at them any more
because she said I had torn them.
I said I hadn't and she said,
'Don't lie.'
So I said,
'OK, I won't look at the football programmes.'

Dad used to take us out sometimes.
He took us to the park
and to see 'The Jungle Book.'
But then one weekend he just
took me somewhere
and left the other two kids at home.
He took me to Tower Bridge.
It was rubbish.
It never opened when they said it would
and anyway you couldn't go up the towers that day
either.
When we got back
I heard Sue having a go at him
for not taking the others.
He said he could just take me if he wanted to.
She said that he was living with her family now

so that meant taking all the kids.
I said it was rubbish anyway
and Sue said,
'Listen to him
he doesn't even say thank you.'
'Don't blame me,' says Dad,
'that's his mother's doing.'
'Oh, there's no need to tell me about her,'
says Sue.

After that he never took me out on my own again.

Sometimes we all went over to Nan's.
She used to take me on one side and give me
something
like a bit of money
or an old medal thing that belonged to grandad.
I used to keep the medal thing next to my bed.
Sue's boy asked me where I got it from
and I told him.
He tells Sue
and she went nuts.
She started shouting at Dad,
telling him that Nan had no right to do that
and she wasn't to treat the kids differently
or we wouldn't go over there.
The medal disappeared not long after that.
I said Sue's boy nicked it
and he said he didn't.
I told Dad
and he said to him,
'Did you nick it?'
and Sue said
that was typical of him to take sides,
and anyway, giving me the medal
was bound to lead to trouble.
I said,
'I want my medal back.'

Mum said one night
she was going to be out on Tuesdays and Thursdays,
and I had to go to Dad's.
She said there wasn't anywhere else I could go.
I couldn't go to Nan's because
her and Nan weren't speaking
and Mum said she couldn't afford a babysitter.
So Tuesday and Thursday nights
Dad came to call for me,
and brought me back about three hours later.
Sue said she didn't see why she should have to cook
one more meal on Tuesdays and Thursdays
just to do Mum a favour.
So Dad said:
'Well, I'll take him up his Nan's.
And Sue said he wasn't going up there
with just me,
it was all three or none.
So I stayed and when she made hamburgers
they were brilliant.
One night Sue said,
'The trouble with your mother
is that she wanted your dad to be a slave.
He had to do just what she wanted or it wasn't good
    enough.
He didn't have a mind of his own.
In the end he just flipped –
he couldn't take it anymore.
She never looked after you properly anyway.
Look at the way she's trying to dump you off on us.'

Mum said one night:
'Are you all right at Dad's?'
I said, 'OK.'
'Do they ever talk about me?'
I said,
'Sue says you don't look after me properly

and you tried to make Dad into your slave.'
Mum said,
'Don't talk to me about Sue.
She was my best friend, you know.
She knows every little detail about my life.
I told her everything about me and your Dad,
week in week out,
and all the time she was seeing him.
On the same night as your Dad said
he was living with her
she had been here earlier
listening to me saying what a bastard he was.
She sat there going
Yes, I'm sure he is,
it must have been terrible.
That's what I've had to put up with,
do you see?'
I said, 'Yes.'

A few days later
I went into Mum's bedroom
to find a clean shirt
and I saw my medal on her table.
I stared at it
for ages,
then I took it to my room and hid it in
my Monopoly box.

Next Tuesday night,
I tore up
all of Sue's boy's football programmes.
Sue smacked me across the face
and said it showed what a little bastard I was.
Dad said he was sick and tired of the things I do and
anyway it was time to go back to Mum's now.
I said I didn't want to go back
so he grabbed me
and I bit his arm.

He went completely spare and belted me
and said I ought to do as I was told.
I started screaming and said
I didn't want to go home.
Dad just picked me up, chucked me in the car
and took me home.

The next night, after tea
I said I wanted to ring Dad.
Mum said I couldn't.
I said I could if I wanted to
he was my dad.
She said,
'You're not going to ring that place.'
So I just went over to the phone and started to dial the
    number
and she grabbed it out of my hand.

On Thursday night
Mum said,
'Your father'll be calling for you earlier tonight
and you'll have to stay the night.'
I said,
'I don't want to go there.
I hate it there.'
Mum said,
'You just have to,
there's nothing else to it, son.
I'm sorry, but there it is.'

When Dad came for me
I wasn't there.
I went to Nan's.

I'm sixteen now
and still with Nan.
I let Mum and Dad
come and see me sometimes.

Once I was ten; one day, maybe, I'll be thirty-five and one day maybe I'll be seventy. You could take me at those three different times and I'd be three different people. But at the same time I'd be the same person. The same person changes himself to become the same person. I keep becoming different and discovering I'm the same. Does this boy know he's changed? He talks like he doesn't know anything. Question: Can cabbages change?

This girl is wild. I often listen to this last thing at night,
wondering where she is, how she survives. Maybe she's a
millionaire now . . . or a dosser. One or the other.

I went to a good school.
I don't actually know if it was good or not
it was just that everyone round our way
said it was good.
I liked the teachers there
and they seemed to like me.
Sounds all right, doesn't it?
But it wasn't.
It all turned into a nightmare.
If you could see me,
if you could talk to me
you could make up your mind straightaway
about what kind of a girl I am.
You would be able to say just where
I fit in.
You know how you can tell
after about two minutes of talking to someone
whether their Dad does a job where he gets his hands
    dirty
or not,
whether they've got a Mum who corrects the way they
    speak.
Some Mums and Dads try to help their kids do
    brilliantly.
and it works – they do brilliantly.
While some parents try like crazy to make their kids do
brilliantly
but the kids are dozos all the same.
Mine were like that.

They were desperate for me to do well
and I didn't.
Every night I would get it:
If you want to get anywhere in life
you have to do well at school.
I got it from the day I started.
You've got to learn how to read and write
you've got to spell
you've got to do your sums
you've got to behave yourself
you've got to do just what the teacher tells you.

And I did behave myself.
I did just what the teacher told me
I remember all through infants I was a goody-goody.
I used to have these little patent leather shoes
and my hair in ribbons
and I changed my knickers every day
and I didn't bite my nails.
I helped the teacher clear up after school
and I always said please and thank you
and the whole thing
was a waste of time.
It did me no good at all.
I could scarcely read or write.

We had these books about little goblins
and some wore red and some wore blue
and some wore yellow
and every book was about more of these horrible little
    goblins.
They didn't do anything
they just sat about in the woods
saying look there's a red goblin
hallo I'm a blue goblin.
Then they used to give us bits of paper with,
Hallo I'm a blue (. . .)
and you had to write in 'goblin'.

I always wrote globlin.
I didn't give a stuff about goblins.
The other kids moved on to books about dragons
and ballet dancers but I was stuck with the goblins.

Every night I'd come home with
a goblin book and my Dad would make me read it to
    him.
If I stopped or stumbled he would say,
'You've got to learn it,
If you don't you'll be on the junk heap.'
I tried,
but it just never stuck together.
I say 'never'
that's not true
I did learn to read
and I did learn to write
but it was never like the other kids.
It was never like the ones who could pick up
a piece of paper or a book
and read it just like that.
When we were told to write something
like 'What I Did at the Seaside'
all the other kids would be head down scribbling away –
and I'd be nowhere.
So I gave up.
I started mucking about.
I got in with this other girl
who giggled all the time
and talked about boys and pop singers.
That's all we talked about
all day –
boys and pop singers.
We were only ten.
She knew hundreds of rude jokes and songs
that she had got from her elder sister.

My friend Billy's
got a ten foot willy
he showed it to the girl next door
she thought it was a snake
so she hit it with a rake
and now it's only four foot four

and things like that.

She was common
I was not so common
but I made myself as common as her.
My parents saw it happening and went spare.
They told me I wasn't allowed to play with her.
They tried to make the teacher not let us sit together
or play together
but we found ways round it.
And we went on giggling.

The teachers changed towards me now.

Because I didn't do as I was told
and I was cheeky
and didn't do my work
they stopped being nice to me.
I knew I was going nowhere
and I could see which kids were going somewhere
and I could see which ones were going a long way.
But though I could see it
I couldn't do anything about it.
I had tried
but it hadn't worked
So now at least it was fun
if I could get with my friend
and we could be cheeky
and get down the back and giggle.

The teachers
(like I said) were very nice

in a sort of a way.
Of course none of them lived round our way
because who would if they could help it?
They all drove in, in their little cars,
and waved to us out of their windows.
Then at going home time
they climbed into their little cars and
waved to us and disappeared off.
I used to wonder where they went.

I used to think they all lived in the same place.
They all lived in a place that looked like a house on TV.
Table clothes on the table
and gardens.
I imagined they were all there in this one house
wandering in and out.

But if I ever saw a row of posh houses
like when we went on the train
I'd think that they lived in a row of houses like that
with trees outside and front gardens.
And if I went past they would look out of the windows
and wave to me as I walked past
just as they did when they waved out of their car
    windows.

It was just about this time
I discovered things.
I discovered that some of the kids' parents in my class
used to see some of the teachers out of school.
You'd hear a teacher say,
'Tell your father that I won't be able to make it on
    Saturday.'
Or
'Could you take this note to your mother?'
It was all very quiet
nothing shouted about
it was just there.

The name on the envelope didn't say Mrs Jones
like when a letter came home to my mum
it just said 'Janet'.
Then you'd notice something to do with photos and
    books.
We'd be doing something in class like transport
and one of the kids would bring in a book
or a photo of some place
and when you looked in the book
it said
'I thought you might find this useful,
John.'

And after school
it would
be 'Thanks for the book, John.'

My dad knew all about transport
he was a lorry driver
but no one said to him:
'Thanks, Dave, for telling us about transport.'
It was just:
'Your daughter is causing us problems.'
And I was.

I used to find excuses to wander around school,
go to the toilet
find my hairband
see a girl about her bracelet she lost
and I was always looking at comics and magazines.

Teachers started shouting at me.
'I'm just about as sick and tired of you
as it's possible to be.'
'You've got about as much sense as a bit of wood.'
'If you used your brain half as much as you used your
    tongue
you'd be a genius.'
'How dare you talk like that to me?'

'For the last time,
STOP GIGGLING.'
'I heard that, I heard that.
Once more and you'll be out.'

I learnt how to sulk and scowl.
I could twist my lips round
and make my eyes go dead
if anyone started telling me off,
and if anyone touched me to move me on
or get me out of a seat
I'd shout,
'Get your hands off me!'
'DON'T TOUCH ME!!'
because I knew they're not allowed to touch you.

When I left that school
they had a party
and I got hold of this bottle of fizzy orange and shook it
    up
and then I squirted it all over the place
so they threw me out.
I wasn't allowed to stay for the party.
I had mucked up some pictures on the wall
and ruined someone's dress.
So I didn't say goodbye to anyone
I just left.
That summer my parents got sick of me hanging about
    at home
and started letting me play out a lot more.
I used to meet with my friend
and we'd stand about on the edge of the playground
at the back of the flats and call out at boys,
and then run for it.
I could stay out after tea as well
and my parents never knew where I was.
They weren't bothered as long as it was light.

They thought no harm could come to us
if it wasn't dark.

One evening
we climbed into the old school.
We walked about giggling
and saying rude things about the teachers
as if they were there.
And one of us would pretend to be a teacher
and the other of us would say rude things to them.
We pretended to be in charge of assembly
and all the kids were going mad.
It was so funny.
I stood there saying:
'I'm just about as sick and tired of you
as it's possible to be.'
'You've got about as much sense as a bit of wood.'
'If you used your brain
half as much as you used your tongue
you'd be a genius.'
And we laughed and laughed and laughed.

So for the next few nights
we crept into school.
We never got caught
because we knew a way in.

Then one night,
we were in the staff room
with our feet up –
pretending to be smoking
at playtime,
and I pretended to be one of the kids that
takes the tea out to the teacher on duty in the
    playground.
I was rummaging about in the cupboard when I
found this box of matches.
So I said,

'Let's burn some stuff in the sink.'
So we started burning bits of old newspaper
in the sink.
There was a big stack of papers
and we started tearing off strips
and burning them.
Then we started twirling round and round with the
    burning strips.
The fire went out
but it glowed.
We made these big red and black circles round us.
Bits were falling to the ground.
So I said after a while,
'We'd better clear this stuff up.'
I looked around for a brush but I couldn't find one –
so instead we started pushing the mess under an old sofa.
We pushed all the bits of burnt newspaper
across the floor and under the sofa.
Then we went next door to the music room.
Everything was locked away except for some broken
    marraccas,
so we made up a dance.
We were like disco dancers
and we were in a row and dancing, using the marraccas
and singing.

Suddenly I heard this cracking sound.
I said,
'Oh no, someone's coming.
Shuttup!'
And we listened.
But it wasn't someone coming
It was just a cracking noise.
We went to the door and looked out
and there was smoke pouring out of the staff room.
The corridor was already full of it.
I looked the other way

but it's a dead end.
The music room is the last room in the corridor.
My friend started screaming and crying
and I said we've got to run for it
but she wouldn't move.
We couldn't climb out of the window,
they were too high up.
I said we've got to run for it
but she just went on screaming
so I said
I'm going
and she was sobbing and screaming and choking
and I didn't wait anymore
and I ran.
As I went past the staffroom I could see
it was blazing in there
so I turned and shouted
for her to come but all I could hear was her screaming.
A moment later there was a huge explosion,
an enormous bang
and a great crashing of wood and bricks.
and I ran home.

My friend's name was Sharon.

If you could see me
I wonder what you'd describe me as now.

She is indescribable. Someone who knows the answers to everything. Someone who can pretend to be anyone because she doesn't know who she is. She could tell this story seven different ways depending on what day of the week it is.

This boy must be about fifteen. Angry with everything. He'll burn himself out by the time he's twenty. I can hear him walking about while he's talking. He's probably waving his arms around. Mad eyes.

Sometimes I think I'm really old
and nearly an adult
and other times
I can remember when I was a kid
and it only seems like yesterday
and I am still that little kid.
Something that happened five years ago
still burns me up.
It's as if it's me
it happened to.
Well of course it is me,
isn't it?

My best friend's house was at the end of my road.
It was by an alley-way
where men on the way to the station in the mornings
took a short cut.
My best friend's dad was one of those men.
He had eight black suits in his wardrobe.

I hated my best friend's mother.
At first
I thought it was because she had a gold tooth
in her face
but that was only part of it.
The only thing I could say about her
if anyone asked me,
'why do you hate her?'
was,

'She pretends to be jolly
when she isn't jolly.'
She was very jolly with her dog
and kept saying:
'Oh you lovely great big fellow
voo voo voo,'
down its nose.
I don't think that dog liked that very much
though she bought it a box of chocolates every week
and an ice lolly when it was hot.

When I came
she used to say,
'Hilloo, delling,'
which no one else ever did.
No one else called me delling.

'You won't go into the lounge, will you?'
she'd say.
Every time.
'You won't go into the lounge, will you?'
There was never any reason why we'd want to go in the
    lounge.
You sometimes saw it through the door.
Everything in there was shiny.
The chairs, the sofa, the walls.
All shiny.
'You won't go in the lounge, will you?'
You're not kidding, lady,
we won't go in the lounge all right.

Also we weren't allowed to go out on Sundays.
I was allowed to go and see my friend
but he wasn't allowed to come and see me.
When I came over
we had to stay in his room
or in the garden.
Once I asked her,

'Why can't we go out on Sunday and play?'
and she said,
'Because it's Sunday.'

When we were in the garden
we had to play at the bottom
in the hedge.
If we played anywhere else
we would spoil the flowers,
spoil the lawn,
spoil the compost heap.
There were two sheds
but we weren't allowed in either of them.

When visitors came
I was sent home.

Once I saw her having tea with our teacher
in the Olde Oake Tea Roomes.
As I walked past the door
both of them at the same time
had opened their mouths
and they had tiny pieces of cake
they were prodding in
off their red nails.

I wasn't given cake at my friends
because she once heard
that what I liked was
cream crackers.
Once a week she said,
'Look,
I'm getting out the tin of cream crackers for you,'
and she kept opening and shutting the cupboard door
and
getting out the special plates with flowers on the edge
and she would put two cream crackers on the plate
and stand next to me
watching me eat

asking me the whole time,
'Do you really like cream crackers?
Why do you like cream crackers?
How wonderful it is
to see a little fellow like you
enjoying a nice cream cracker!!
It does me good to see youngsters
like you
having such a good time.'

When I had finished two cream crackers
she would sit waiting for me to say
thank you
and I always said,
'Thank you,
that was really very nice,
thank you.'

Then she said,
'No no no
Don't be silly dear
it was nothing.'
Then she put the tin of cream crackers away.
I came to hate
cream crackers.

One week
I tried to say that I didn't want any.
She said,
'What?
You don't want your cream crackers?
But I got them especially for you.
This is your tin of cream crackers.
No one else eats them
You must have your cream crackers
I save them for you, dear.
I can't imagine a week
without you having your cream crackers.

Go on.
Have just one
if you're full up.'

I said, 'I really don't think I could manage it
but it's very nice of you.'

So she started up all over again
about how
ever since I first came to the house
I had loved cream crackers.
In fact,
it was difficult to think of me
without thinking of a cream cracker
and once –
which all goes to show –
she had even called me cream cracker
and here they all were
fresh out of the tin
surely I ought to have one
now that she had gone to all the bother
of getting them out for me.

It was so difficult.
Should I go through listening to her
going on and on and on
or should I finish the whole thing off
by cramming a cracker into my mouth?

The only thing that stopped me cramming
was thinking that if I looked too keen
about one
she'd think I wanted another one
and I'd have to eat that one as well.
So I picked up the cracker
pretending not to notice
she was watching me.
I broke a piece off.
I put it into my mouth

and it sat there like an old match box.
It was in there:
a whole dry matchbox.
I tried to turn the match box over
to make it softer
but all those thank-yous
and no-thank-yous
and little smiles between the thank-yous
had dried my mouth out.
I could not turn the match-box over.

She said,
'There, your old favourite –
cream crackers.'
I nodded
and kept my mouth shut
as the matchbox inside started bending.
The trouble was
I had broken off a piece
that was exactly the size of the roof of my mouth.
It had got caught there
locked between the teeth at the back.
I couldn't curl my tongue back far enough
to get it out
and I couldn't peel it back from the front
with my tongue.
It was just jammed there
between the teeth.

My friend's mother was watching me very closely now
and still pretending not to.

The match box was completely stuck.
If I sucked
it just moved closer to the red bit
that hangs down at the back of your mouth.
I couldn't roll my tongue up
and get at it from behind

54

but I was trying to.
There was loads of spit coming into my mouth
but all the time I kept my mouth shut tight
because I had once heard her say
if there was one thing she hated in this world
it was seeing into other people's mouths.

I went on lifting up my tongue
to the biscuit
stuck in the roof of my mouth.
It felt like a piece of cardboard.
I started to feel my throat
trying to climb into my mouth.
The whole match box suddenly moved backwards
and hit the red bit at the back.
I said
AAARKG.
My mouth went wide open
and I stuffed my finger in there,
and pulled the cracker out from my teeth.
It fell on to the flowery plate
in several small soggy bits of cream cracker.

My friend's mother stopped talking,
looked at the pieces on the plate
and looked at my mouth.
I was still busy clearing up the mess in there
left behind after the cracker had flown out.

I couldn't say I was sorry
or more cracker would have fallen out
so I just waved my hand in the air
ducked my head down
nearly as low as the table
and waited for the rest to go down.

I don't remember much more.

Mind you,
a month later

the whole school was sent home early
because the boilers burst.
When me and my friend got to his house
his mother was coming in
from eating cakes at the Olde Oake Tea Roomes.
My friend tells her
why we had to come home early
and she turns to me and says,
'Where will you be eating, dear?'
I said,
'I don't know
I suppose I'll eat at the caff.'
So she says,
'Do you have the money?'
I said, 'Yes,'
which wasn't true.
I didn't have any money
and she said,
'Good.'
Then she put my friend in front of her
at the gate
pulled her lips right back
showing her gold tooth
and said,
'Run along, then, dear.
Bye bye.'

Some people.

I'm angry about
windows you can't open,
crowded trains
when I can't read my own writing
losing my watch
pigeon shit

I don't like listening to this. She must be about sixteen.

Some white boys got into an empty flat
and made it their den.
There were loads of empty flats
boarded up
but anyone could get in.
There was one on our balcony that tramps
used to sleep in.
It stank.
It really stank something awful.

My mum said the boys meant trouble
as soon as she saw them.

To start off with
they didn't do much,
they just went in there and sang songs
and banged about.
It didn't seem to matter much,
we thought the council was going to come
and do all the flats up soon
so then they'd be chucked out.
But of course they didn't.

Water used to run right down the wall –
that's all four floors.
In the winter it made a great big sheet of ice
with huge icicles at the top.

The boys didn't come from the estate,
my dad said they came from near the football ground
but he doesn't always know what's going on.

They used to shout at us,
call us all the usual names

but there's nothing strange about that –
people who look much nicer than they do
call us the same names.
We just pretend we don't hear.

There must have been about ten of them,
they didn't sleep there
they just made it their den for evenings
and weekends.

My dad's cousin had dog's mess
stuffed through his letter box.
I say it was dog's mess
but it could have been theirs.
Of course I don't know it was them that did it,
it's just a guess.

This happened the week after a meeting.
They had a meeting at my school.
It was voting time in the elections
and they had someone up for it
so they got permission to have a meeting
in our school on a Saturday.

One plan was for lots of people to stop them.
We could all stand outside and stop them getting in
but other people said it would be better if
we just pretended we didn't know they were there.
They said, people like that just want a fuss made about
  them
and that's what gets people joining them.
So in the end nobody did anything.

But the next week was when the dog's mess got put
  through
my dad's cousin's place –
and there was more.
They cut up a boy.
He was coming back from the club

and they jumped on him
and cut his face up.
He's all right now.

After that they got bolder.
They used to stand by the bins at the bottom of the
    staircase
and jump out at people.
They didn't want money.
One woman was coming back from the market
and she had two big bags of stuff
and they jumped on her.
She started screaming,
'Take the money, take the money,'
but they just took the bags off her
and threw it all over the place.
All the oranges and mangoes and potatoes –
they just threw them all over the place.
They didn't want the money.

On the way back from school was bad.
You never knew whether they'd be there or not.
I stopped doing jewellery after school.
I didn't dare come home late
because I knew they'd be there.
They were there sometimes even if I came back early.

I came round the corner of the yard
and they were standing at the bottom of my staircase.
I just felt sick.
I had nowhere to go
except past them.
So I had to walk towards them across the yard
and all the time they were grinning.
When I got to them they just stood in my way.
I couldn't speak or say anything at all,
I was just rigid.
And I could smell them.

I hope you don't think this rude but
where I come from we don't eat fish
if it's older than one day.
Fish that's older than that is bad fish.
But here you eat very old fish
and it smells.
Fish that you eat
doesn't smell where I come from.
So people who eat fish here
smell of bad fish.
Maybe you don't notice
but I do
and it sometimes makes me feel sick.
I don't say anything
I just turn away.
These boys smelt of bad fish.

They started saying things to me –
you know the sort of thing
it was lies, all of it,
they were just saying it to see me look embarrassed.
Then one of them undid his zip
and flashed it.
The others loved it
they laughed so much
and they said one day they'd come and get me.

I didn't say a thing
I didn't show anything on my face
at least I don't think I did.
They went on calling me names
and one of them tried to push me against
the boy who was flashing.
I didn't scream
I just put my arms up to protect myself
and so all they did was spit at me.
They let me through
and just spat at me.

Before they went home at night
they used to run along the balconies kicking the doors in.
We'd be in bed
and suddenly you'd wake up
with this huge crash and roaring noise.

They had just kicked your door in.

We put big bolts and locks on the door after that
so instead of the door flying open next time
they just kicked it to pieces.

That's how the little boys downstairs died.
One night they kicked the doors in
and threw in some burning stuff
and the flat burnt out.
Their mum and dad couldn't get to them in time.
It was mad.

Some people came down and said they'd help us
and then they went away again.

But there was a meeting at the club.
Mum said I wasn't to go
but I went.
Some people said we had to keep our dignity
and not be rushed into doing anything hasty.
I thought that was right,
that's what I had done when the boys stood at the
    bottom of my staircase,
and someone said
we should do what we did when they came to my school,
how we had ignored them.
But then someone else stood up and said
that was a mistake.
It was because we ignored them that they got brave.
Then someone else said we should take up arms
and fight to the bitter end or something
and it just made people laugh

because he was very old and it sounded like people back
  home.
And then everyone voted on something
and that was it.

I went home and couldn't stop thinking about it.
I went over and over what people said.
First I thought about it from one side
then the other.
And then bit by bit it came clear to me.
I knew what had to be done.

It all seemed so simple
and yet no one had thought of it before.

All I needed was help.
I knew who I could trust
and I just went to see them.
All through the week.
I talked and
I talked and talked and talked.
I don't know how I got it in me to do it
but I did.
I talked and talked and talked
so by the time Friday night came round
there was a whole crowd of us
who had agreed.

We waited for them to go home.
For some reason they didn't kick our doors in
that Friday night.
They just went home drunk
and then we went into their den.
Maybe there was forty of us
maybe there was more.
Now I think of it
there must have been.
We had to break the padlock

they had put on the door
but my dad had a saw that can saw through metal.

Inside it was amazing.
They had pictures and flags up all over the place
and they had scribbled stuff on the walls.
There were hundreds and hundreds of beer cans.
You could tell that they used to play a game
where they piled them up
and aimed at them to make them fall down.
We walked about looking at it all,
the flags and the pictures of their heroes.

After a bit we just took everything down
and cleared up.
Then we sat down and waited until the morning.
It was a long night,
some people slept a bit
leaning on each other's shoulders,
some people talked very quietly in the corner.
As the light came up in the morning
I remember looking out across the yard
and I saw myself walking across there
towards the boys at the bottom of the staircase
and everything that I had bottled up then
came flooding out.
I had been so good at pretending that
I didn't care
and they hadn't hurt me
and now, with everything else going on
and all the bad things that had happened,
I just couldn't stop myself
I just wept.

We expected them to come at about eleven.
But we weren't sure
that's why we had been there all night.
They used to meet there before going off
to a football match.

So we waited.
Some people went out and came back with food and
    drink for us
and we cleaned out the rest of the place.
Then two of them appeared.

They suddenly seemed so small,
with their skinny little legs.
We heard them coming up the staircase
singing,
they came round the corner on to the balcony
and we rushed out at them.
I'll never forget their faces.
Their eyes went all goggly
and they just turned round and ran for it.

A huge cheer went up
and people started to dance and sing and jump about.
It suddenly seemed funny.

And then it happened again
This time it was five or six of them.
We watched them cross the yard,
we heard them coming up the stairs
and then we rushed out at them
and away they ran.

After this
people began to collect on the stairs and the balcony.
There were people looking out from the flats
on the other side of the yard.
So we started saying,
come and join us,
come and fill up the balcony,
fill up the staircase.

Well then you learnt
who was on your side or not.
And all sorts came –

Some I didn't expect.
An old white lady came up
and talked and cried a lot
about the last war and her husband.
I didn't understand all of it
but he had seen terrible things in the prison camps,
he hadn't been in one himself,
he had just seen them at the end of the war.
Anyway
it was soon full of people
when the caretaker turned up.

He said we weren't allowed in the flat
it was against the law
and unless we got out
he would call the police.
So we said,
how come you didn't call the police
when the boys were in here, then?
and he didn't have much of an answer to that one
so he went off swearing.

And that was it.
It was that simple.

Well, some of us
stayed there,
we took it in turns.
We had some dustbin lids
and sticks at the ready
to sound an alarm in case anybody came
but they never came back.

I just hope that wherever they are now
someone does the same as we did.

Whenever I've been faced with anything I run.

This is a very sweaty guy. I'd guess about fourteen.

She was the first girl I fancied.
I used to watch her across a room.
There was nothing I could do to stop myself
I just used to watch her.
It made me unhappy just watching.
How do you know what someone's like
if all you do is watch them?
I should have talked to her
but I didn't know how.
I couldn't find a way to start chatting.
I had never really noticed her when I was lower down
in the school
and now I did notice her
I didn't know how to say:
'Hallo, I've noticed you.'
I couldn't find a way to start,
so all I did was watch her.
I know it sounds crazy,
here I was seeing her every day,
but there was no way I could actually say anything,
to her.
Anyway,
if I had've tried.
everyone would have noticed.
They'd've been all round me
leering and jeering
saying,
'Ha, ha, you fancy her.'
And I'd've just died.
I'd've felt like crawling away
with them all laughing and grinning at me.

I could see it,
me saying to her,
'Hallo, interesting pen you've got there –
Hallo, I've just noticed that when you walk
you put your feet on the ground,'
and everyone looking round and staring at me.
But what could I say to her?
How could I find something that seemed
like I really did have something to say to her?
Did I have something to say to her?
Or did I just want to watch her?
Maybe that was it
all I wanted to do was watch her.
Maybe deep down I didn't really want to talk to her
I didn't want her to be a person,
maybe I just wanted her to be an ad on the telly
that you could watch again and again
and never really meet.
Oh, I don't know
what I thought
it was agony
all the watching
and not wanting to be watching.

I got crazy about little things she did
or some part of her.
It was terrible,
like I broke her up into little bits.
I know this sounds strange
but I was mad about the way she closed her eyes.
Now isn't that crazy?
Her eyelids seemed to meet in the middle
of her eye,
I mean her top eyelid came down a long way to meet
her bottom eyelid.
And it did it slowly
sometimes when she was speaking

so that she looked kind of sleepy.
Now how could that be something
that you could be crazy about someone for?
I don't know.
I just used to watch her from the side
and try and figure out why her eyes
made me feel all hot.

Worst of all was thinking about
clothes, no clothes, dressing, undressing.
It all seemed so mysterious and secret,
and unimaginable.
I couldn't really believe she ever really did undress.
It seemed like some fantastic thing
that would be wonderful and amazing
if it did happen but of course it didn't
because she was really always dressed.
Other people undressed;
I did,
people in films did,
but she didn't.
Underneath her clothes there was a naked body
but it never became naked.
And then the moment I thought
there was this naked body underneath
I could never stop myself trying to imagine
what it would look like.
But all I had to go on were pictures of other people.
But she wasn't these other people,
she was her and she didn't look anything like
these other people.

I've looked at pictures of women.
When they've got no clothes on at all
it all fits together.
You realise how it's all joined together.
That's obvious
but so much of the time

you don't see how it all fits together.
They have pictures of women with only the top half
or they have pictures of women with little bits of clothes
    on
and it breaks it all up.
You can't see how it all fits together.
And when people wear clothes
it's even worse
you just can't see how one bit flows into the next.
I mean, backs don't seem to have much to do with bums.
A shirt or a jumper covers a back
then there's a belt
and there's a skirt
or jeans.
But when you see a picture of someone
completely naked
the back and the bum are joined together.
Obviously.
We all know that
but I had never seen a girl or a woman's back and bum.
I just had to imagine it.

But for it to really happen,
for me to be able to really see it
was just impossible.
It was like I thought
I would never in the whole of my life
ever see it.
She was always dressed.
and that was all there was to it.

The thing that really hurt
was when the girls came in from gym and games
and they had showers.
She had showers!
You can't have showers with your clothes on.
It meant that just a few minutes before –
she had actually been standing there

with no clothes on
and water pouring all over her.
How come the water
could get a chance to be there
and I couldn't?
And then, even more fascinating –
all the other girls knew what she looked like
but I didn't.
What was so special about them?
How come they had all those chances
and I didn't?
I'd sometimes look at them and try and pretend
I had their eyes.
I was one of them
and I could see what they had just seen.
If only I could make them
take the video of what they had seen
out of their brains and put it into mine
and play it back.

But she wasn't a video.
She was there
on the other side of the room
talking and moving about.
She was nothing to do with me,
she didn't even really know I existed
and she certainly had no idea of what I thought.
She belonged to herself
and I didn't have anything.

But what did I want?
I didn't know.
Sometimes I thought
all I actually wanted was just to stare at her
with no clothes on.
It would be just enough for her
to come into my room at home
and take all her clothes off

stand there
put all her clothes on and go.
Or maybe I would walk into the girls' showers
after school and
there was only me and only her
and she would be having a shower.
Would I have no clothes on?
No, I wouldn't dare.
That's the trouble.
I'd be afraid.
I'd want to put my hands over my crotch,
I don't know why
I couldn't bear anyone to stare at me,
It almost feels like if anyone was staring at it too much
it'd fall off.
And anyway they might laugh.
But what if she said
she would only take her clothes off
if I took off all mine?
I would be so jumpy about myself
I'd be feeling
I wouldn't be able to take in everything about her.

I hadn't even spoken to her
But then the way it was going to happen
wasn't going to be because I actually spoke to her.

It was going to happen just by chance.
We would be on an aeroplane together
and the aeroplane would crash on a desert island
and everyone would be killed except me and her
and we would wander about the island together
and she would think I was fantastic and
she would spend all day by the sea taking her clothes off.

We also got parts in a film
and I was the hero and wore jackets with the collar
    turned up

and she burst into my studio flat
and started undressing
and then we had loads of love scenes to do together
except no one was going to see me completely naked all
   over
in a film.

I started to make plans
about how I could go out with her.

I found out her phone number by going through all
the people with her name in the phone book
until I found someone with her address.
I used to sit by the phone
with her number on a piece of paper in my hand
and start conversations with her.
Hi, it's me
Look I know this'll come as a surprise
but
would you like to come out with me?

Hi
would you like to go ice skating?

Hi
would you like to go to Macdonalds?

Hi
can I come over to your house
and see you undress?

Hi
don't you think I sound natural?
Yes I do.
In a minute I'm going to ask you out
but before I do
I'm going to go on pretending to sound natural
then when I think you think I'm really nice
I'm going to say
do you want to come out?

And you're going to say
you're going to say . . .
you're going to burst out laughing
and point at my crotch and say
what do you call that then?
And I'm going to say
it wasn't my idea to take all my clothes off
the idea was that you take all your clothes off.

I sometimes thought
the best thing would be to write her a letter:
Please don't tell anyone I am writing this letter
but I've got to write it because I think
you're really nice and I would like you
to come and see a film with me.
Or
This letter must be a complete surprise to you.
Actually it's a bit of a surprise for me, too,
I don't know how I got round to writing it
but here I am writing it. Huh!
I'd just like to say that I think you're fantastic
and I'm pathetic and oh no I don't know what to say
except drivel on and on and on . . .
Or
I've tried to write you loads of times
and now I've finally got round to it.
I'm sorry about my writing
but when you're thinking about someone taking her
    clothes off
it makes it hard to concentrate and have you ever
    thought
of going up in an aeroplane and crashing on a desert
    island
because then you'd think I was terrific
but I couldn't take all my clothes off
but you'd like to take all yours off.
Or

Hi, I enclose a picture of me.
You will recognise me as being someone in your class
at school.
Don't laugh
but I'm crazy about you.
I think you are fantastic
I think you are beautiful.
I often wonder how your back meets your bum –
I mean I know it meets your bum
but I've never actually seen it
and I often try to imagine it.
Of course you know what it's like
but I don't and it's driving me crazy
but one day soon we will be in a film together
and I'm playing the lead part.
One night I'm lying in bed and you come into my
    bedroom
and take all your clothes off.
It's great, isn't it?
See you in school tomorrow.
Oh it was hopeless
I couldn't write a thing.

The worst times were when I was on my own
in bed
in the bath
or just in the house on my own.
Give me half an hour on my own
I'd be thinking about her
and the old hand'd go down the trousers
and I'd be at it.
I just couldn't stop myself.
I didn't want to stop myself.
My mind would be full of her
it would start off with me thinking about
seeing her neck
or remembering when her skirt had blown up a bit

in the wind
and then she'd be looking at me
and I thought harder and harder about the skirt blowing
    up
and I'd be going at it so hard my arm ached
but I couldn't stop,
it's like there's a magnet there
and I'd stop just before the end
and it all burst from inside without me doing anything.

Then she went from my mind
and I didn't think about her for a few hours
until next time I was on my own
and it would start all over again.

If only I could meet her out of school sometime
and then I could say something to her.
I used to go down her street
and pretend to be walking somewhere
so that by chance I might just bump into her
when I walked past her house.
I used to look the other way as if I didn't know
there was anything special about that house,
so if she came out
I could say, 'Hi I was just going over my friend's house.
Do you live here, then?
Oh, by the way, I've always thought you're fantastic
and I fancy you an awful lot
and I wondered if you would like to come out with me?
And afterwards we could go back to your house
and no one would be in and you'd start taking your
    clothes off.'

But I never did see her.
I don't know how many times I walked down her road
she was never there.

In the end
I did write to her.
This is what I said:

Hi,
I suppose this letter will come as a complete surprise.
I've thought you're really nice for a long time,
but I didn't know how to say it.
I wanted to ask you out
but there are always people about
and I can't stand people listening
to private things, can you?
Anyway, I'd like to ask you out.
I don't suppose you want to come and see
a football match but there's loads of films on,
aren't there? I'll meet you at the clock tower
five o'clock Saturday if you're interested.

And I actually sent it.
On the Friday.
She'd get it in the morning
and then I'd have all day to get through.
It was hell.
I kept thinking of all the different things that could
  happen:
She hadn't got the letter
and I'd turn up and she wouldn't be there.
But she'd get it on Monday
and bring the letter to school
and show all her friends
and they'd come up to me
and say
I liked your letter
and I'd crawl away and die.

Maybe she'd get the letter
but she was going to see her gran
and she couldn't get out of it.
Really she was dying to come
and she couldn't find a way of letting me know
but she sent me a letter
and I'd get this fantastic letter on Monday morning

saying,
I've always thought you were the nicest bloke
I've ever seen
and I've always wanted you to be standing there
looking at me with no clothes on.

Maybe she'd turn up and she'd be with this other bloke
and he stands there saying
don't you go round writing letters like that again
or you'll be in trouble
she's my girl
so hands off

Or maybe she'd be there on her own
and I just wouldn't know what to say
I'd just stand there grinning
and saying what shall we do then?
And she'd say
I don't know
and I'd say
I don't know either
and that would go on for ages
and then she'd go to her place
and I'd go to my place
and that'd be it.
Nothing.

All day
I thought about it.
I watched the sport on the telly
I was so nervous I scarcely had anything to eat
I put on three different tee shirts
two pairs of jeans
and I don't know how many times I wet my hair.

I got to the clock tower about half an hour early,
so I was standing there trying to look cool
for a whole half an hour
and it's really hard trying to look cool

on your own, under the clock tower, for a whole half
  hour.
I tried standing with both legs apart
hands on my hips,
I tried walked up and down, kicking my legs forward,
I tried leaning up against the wall,
I tried whistling
and all the time I was just checking
whether I had that little tufty bit of hair
on the top of my head standing up
because I really hate that tufty bit
and I was trying to smooth it down all the time.

I wanted her to come
when I'd be looking the other way
so it was her that saw me
and I could turn round, go
Oh yeah, hi,
like I wasn't desperate to see her
but just relaxed.
Don't ask me why I shouldn't want to look desperate
or why I shouldn't want to look keen
when in fact I wasn't just keen
but completely crazy.

After about half an hour of this
I began to think
I had made a huge mistake.
Maybe I didn't like her after all.
I stood there trying to remember what she looked like.
It wasn't like when I was at home and I could
fix her in my mind.
She was gone.
I could not think what she looked like.
And then I panicked.
What if she was wearing something
I didn't like?
What if she was all dressed up looking really posh

and I thought it was awful?
Would I still be crazy about her?
And then what were we going to say?
I'd never even spoken to her before.
We couldn't talk about football, could we?
I was in the middle of this panic
when she arrived.
She said;
Did you write that letter?
I said, yeah.
she said,
What did you write it for?
I said,
Cos I wanted to.
She said,
But you must be mad.
I said,
Am I?
She said;
What's the matter with you?
Don't you think black boys are good enough for me?
I said,
I never said that.
She said,
I don't go out with white boys, you know.
I said,
Right,
She said,
Black girls aren't cheap, you know.
You can't just snap your fingers
and think we come running.
I said,
Right.
She said,
We've got minds of our own, you know,
and just 'cos you're white
doesn't mean I'm going to think

oh aren't I lucky
some white boy's asked me out.
I said,
Right.

Then there was a long silence.

She said,
Haven't you got anything to say, then?
I said,
No, not really.
She said,
Well what did you ask me out for?
I said,
I don't know.

She said,
Where were we going to go?
I said,
I don't know.
She said,
Look, I've got to do some shopping for my mum, now,
I don't suppose you want to do that, do you?
And I said,
Right.
She said,
Down the market.
I said,
Mmmm, I get you.
She said,
Right, I'm going, then.
I said,
OK.

And she just kind of shambled off.

I went home
amd lay down on my bed
and punched the pillow for about half an hour.

80

I've invented this extra-sensory device that enables me to read other people's minds. I've needed one for ages. If it doesn't work I will understand nothing. Of course it doesn't work because I haven't invented it but I don't know how I'm going to manage without it. I understand nobody else.

This woman knows too much. I suppose she's nineteen or twenty but if she's sixteen, she definitely knows too much.

The worst thing about it
is that for a time I really liked him.
It would have been so much easier
if I had thought he was horrible.

No
the worst thing
was I thought he was a nice bloke.
Well
he was nice to me
that's what I can't work out.
How could he be nice to me
and still do those things?

It doesn't add up,
well, it doesn't add up for *me*
but in some twisted way
it must add up for *him*.
It's frightening.

I met him outside a cinema.
That's how I got to know him –
sounds mad, doesn't it?
But it's true.

I was stood up.
Some bloke I met at a disco
rang me up and said,
See you at the cinema
at six forty five.
So I turned up.
To be honest

I wasn't that put out
he didn't turn up.
I wasn't that keen on him.
I suppose he thought the same.

You know what I thought
while I was standing there waiting for him?
I thought maybe he was watching me
from over the road.
I had this funny feeling
he was there
in a car
and he could see me standing there waiting for him.

Anyway,
it's not him I'm talking about, is it?
I never saw that one again.
So I am standing there
and it's pretty obvious
I've been stood up.
I'm walking up and down
and I'm looking at my watch and tutting
so it must have been pretty plain to see.
So this feller comes up
and says,
Hasn't he turned up, then?
It didn't sound like a pick-up line.
He sounded quite refined.
I mean he wasn't posh,
he wasn't a toff,
he sounded not rough.
And he was smart without being flashy,
none of those pendants or anything.
So I said,
You guessed it.
So he says,
Me too.
And again I believed him.

He looked kind of blue when he said it.
Me too, he says.
So I said,
(trying to sound a bit funny, I suppose)
My feller and your woman are probably round the
    corner
at the disco.
Do you think so?
he says,
and he sounded so innocent.
Do you think so?
So I laughed.
I was used to blokes trying to come back with some
    clever joke
but he just says,
Do you think so?
So that just egged me on.
I said,
Yeah, I should think so
unless they've made a suicide pact together.
Well
I admit
it wasn't in very good taste,
was it?
And he says.
You're a bit bitter, aren't you?
Oh no, I said,
Don't take any notice of me
it's just a manner of speaking.

Look, he says,
Do you want to see this film?
And I said,
Actually I do.
So he says,
Me too.
Then we looked at each other

84

and I was like giving him the quick once over
checking out he wasn't going to be
a back row groper.
And I reckoned he looked OK.
I don't know what he thought of me
but he said,
What are we waiting for, then?
And I liked him for that.

I bought my own ticket
and we watched the whole film through,
the ads, next week's previews,
the whole lot
and he didn't touch me.
I thought
this bloke seems straight enough.
Maybe I've struck it lucky.

When it finishes,
we get outside
and he says,
Shall I take you home?
It was all so straight
it sounded like my parents or something.
Shall I take you home?
he says,
I've got my car.

I tell you
when you're tossing up in your mind
whether to hang about on your own
at a bus stop at night
or take a lift from someone you know
you don't hang about.
The thing is
I thought I knew him now.
So I said,
Lovely, I'll come in your car
if that's OK

The joke is
I was now trying to be as straight as he was.
I was trying to sound more polite and proper
than I was.
It's terrible to think of it —
I was thinking
I'll try and keep up with this one.
So there's me all of a sudden
all please and thank you.

He takes me to the car
and it's new
and spotless.
You could have eaten your dinner off it.
And it had all those little bits of extras on it,
sun roofs and all that.
He was obviously very proud of it.

And he took me home in it.

I was getting very nosey by now
so I said,
What you do, then
to have a nice little car like this?
He says,
I'm in computers.

Now you only have to say that word
and my mind goes a blank.
Oh nice, I say,
and I have no idea what that means at all.
But I pressed on.
What do you actually do?
It's a bit complicated to explain, he says.
Well don't, chum, I thought.
It's to do with developing some programmes
for use as quality control.

I don't know why I remember him saying that.
I can scarcely remember my own address
and I remember him saying that.

It's to do with developing some programmes
for use as quality control.

Well I do know why I remember it.
Because whenever anyone asked me
when the whole business blew up,
What did he say he did?
I'd say it.
It's to do with developing some programmes
for use as quality control.

But then
that doesn't explain how I remembered it in the first
   place.
Who knows, eh?

And what do you do?
he asked me.
I work in a shop,
I said.
What sort of shop? he says.
A kiddies clothes shop,
I said.
Doesn't it make you broody? he says.
I thought, that's a bit forward for you, isn't it?
No danger of that, I said,
you ought to see them –
they come in there and first thing you hear
is can I have this?
Can I have that?
And the baby's screaming
and there's some kid climbing up the wall.
It's enough to put you off for life.

He dropped me off –
still hadn't touched me.

Shall I see you again? he says.
Get that!
I had never been asked like that before.
Feller, looking out of his car window,
Shall I see you again?

All I'd had
was blokes squashing you up against a shop-window
and saying,
I'll call you when I'll call you
or
Be in next Saturday, right?

So of course
I said,
Yes.
When? he says.
Not during the week, I said,
I'm busy
(trying to sound as if I was someone serious)
and Friday I'm out
(trying to sound as if I was exciting)
but Saturday would be very nice.

Hear me.
. . . would be very nice!
I don't know where I found the chat
I really don't.
Bye,
and that was it.
Of course at the shop on Monday,
with the girls, I was full of it, wasn't I?
I painted him out to be like some film star.
Actually he was quite handsome
but I wasn't going to say to them
actually he's quite handsome.
Oh no.
He was clean

really lovely mouth
wearing a new suit
you could tell he was really strong underneath it
beautiful hands
and his smile
(oh I let them have it).
The way he smiled, I said,
I don't know. I told them
just the way his lips moved over his teeth
it was such a turn on.

And they're all gasping, aren't they?
What about his legs?
What about his legs?
What about his bum?
What about his bum?
To tell the truth
I hadn't had a chance to get much of a look
and I'm a bit of a one for
legs and bums,
but not knowing wasn't going to stop me.
Strong, I said,
but slim,
he's got a great body, girls,
I said,
that's all there is to it.
So, of course, his bum is great – as well.
And what's he do?
Oh, I said,
It's to do with developing programmes
for use as quality control.
It came out
just like that.
That stunned them.
Thank goodness none of them asked me
what it meant.

Anyway, I couldn't stand all this posing
much more.
It's not really my style.
Actually, I don't know anything about him, I said.
For all I know
he could be a go go dancer.
Does he look like a dancer then?
says one of them.
No, I said, trying to bring it all
back down to earth
he just looks like an ordinary nice bloke.

They were furious
they didn't want to hear that, did they?
You're going to say he had a beer gut
and a big soggy bum in a minute.

No no, says one,
She's going to say he was wearing a cardigan.
And then we all fell about.
Mind you
I had to think quick
to see if I could remember whether he was
by chance
wearing a cardigan.
No,
he was not wearing a cardigan
so I carried on laughing.

It's true
he was an ordinary nice bloke.
I have to admit
he wasn't a male pin-up
but he looked OK
and he did have a good body.
I could remember that much.
His jacket didn't just hang on him
like he was a clothes hanger.

He filled it.
Nice.

So I saw him
the next Saturday
and we started going out.
Like me
he lived with his mother
and both our mothers were quite broad minded.
I mean he was nearly twenty
and I was seventeen
so you've got the right, haven't you?

I'd never really been with a bloke before.
I say never really
and I suppose that's a bit of a laugh, isn't it?
You know
how when you're young you say,
Are you a virgin?
She's a virgin
or, she isn't a virgin anymore
and it's either one thing or the other:
either you're a virgin or you're not.

Well it wasn't like that with me.
I mean I'd played about
just to see
in the way that you do.
I was curious.
Anyway
what I'm saying
is that I had never really done it
all the way
and not in a hurry
on a bed at a party
for five seconds before saying
gettoff.

And so I felt different.
I hadn't felt like this before.

I'm not saying it was love
in big letters
I don't think it was.
I wasn't helpless and gooey over him
I just felt kind of grown up
and he was my bloke
and I was his woman
and I got to feeling very randy.
Obviously some of this was down to him –
most of it was down to him, maybe,
but it wasn't only down to him.
Any bloke
I had been going with
for the first time
properly
it would probably have been the same.
It was like I wanted to do it with him
but I looked beyond him to the thing itself.
I wanted 'It'
more than I wanted him.

I don't know what he wanted
I really don't
now I think about it.
I don't think I knew him very well –
well, of course, I didn't know him at all, did I,
if he was someone who could have done those things?

It is terrifying to think about it now.
It's like something coming very slowly to suffocate you.
First you see it coming
then it comes
and then it slowly suffocates you.
Each bit is awful
but each new bit is more terrifying
than the bit before
and you just can't believe that it can get worse
but it does.

The very first hint of it
was a scratch.
He had a scratch on his neck.
Of course you see something like that
when you're in bed with someone,
so I said,
How did you get that?
He says,
What?
I said,
You've got a scratch on your neck.
Have I?
he says,
and he got really bothered.
Bloody hell,
he says,
bloody hell.
I said,
It's not that bad, darling,
well it can't be
if you didn't even know it was there.
But he goes on cursing and blinding away there.

I thought,
Strange bloke,
so he's got a scratch
no need to make a song and dance about it, chum.

But next day
I found myself thinking about it.
Why was he so bothered?
How did he get it?
It ran down his neck
on to his shoulder.
You don't get a scratch like that from
developing some programmes
for use as quality control, do you?
I thought.

Then I thought
he must have got it while he was mending his car.

But then he doesn't mend his car.
He told me he doesn't know the first thing about cars
so he wouldn't have been frigging around underneath
     one.

Next thing that really got to me
was one time when we were talking about his office.
And we were just chatting about
people who are over you and come and check up
you're doing your job
and he suddenly went spare.
He went stark raving bonkers
about this woman who was higher up than he was.
He didn't just slag her off
he went crazy,
his eyes went red
and he clenched his fists
and started shouting about
who the hell does she think she is,
she swaggers in here with her fat arse
and throws her weight about.
And he's getting really tense
and he's saying,
I feel like shoving her out the window
the way she goes on.
I was just sort of agreeing
because I had someone at my shop
who was driving me mad too.

Again it was only afterwards that I started to think
he was bit over the top there, wasn't he?
Not what he said
but how he said it
the look on his face
it was really ugly.

Next thing
he gets his car seats changed.
I got into the car
and I said,
Oh that's nice
you've changed the car seats.
I'm a real sucker for things like that.
And he goes,
Shuttup.
I said,
What did you say?
He says, shuttup.
Do you mind not speaking to me like that.
Listen,
he said,
just because I've changed the car seats
there's no need to make a big deal out of it.
I've changed the car seats
leave it at that, will you?
I said,
Yes,
I will to be sure
I was only making a comment.
I thought you'd be pleased that I liked the look of it,
if you don't want me to pass comments
about things like that
I shall know in future
not to open my big mouth.
I'm sorry, I said,
I'm so sorry.
Weird.
What a weird way to go on.

These things that I'm telling you
fit together now
they all make up a pattern.
At the time

they each didn't mean very much
and they had nothing to do with each other.
I'm not the kind of person
that keeps trying to figure out what's going on.
Maybe that was a fault in me.
I'm sure I'm not like that now
but I was just content
that he turned up when he said he was going to turn up.
We didn't have rows
we went nice places
we had a good sex life
we didn't get on each other's nerves
talking was easy with him
and that was all there was to it.
I was happy it was like that.
I wasn't
spending hours and hours thinking about him
and wondering whether he was this kind of man
or that kind of man
and what did he mean when he said that?
And what did he mean when he said this?
And there wasn't all this game stuff going on, either,
like the girls at the shop coming in and saying,
I'm going to pretend to be out when he rings tonight
or
I showed him this card I got from my old boyfriend
and he went spare.
Ooh I love it seeing him so jealous
it's a real come-on
and all that.
And they pretend this old boyfriend
is really interested
and then they do get interested in the old boyfriend
and then the present guy says he's interested in his old
    girlfriend
and then they're not speaking

and then they're together again
and reunions are really sexy, aren't they?

I'm bored with all that
and we didn't have any of it
it just seemed to be running along smoothly.

We
were watching telly one night
and there was another one of those stabbings on the
    news –
some poor woman had been found in an old tunnel
and a maniac had cut her to pieces.
It was unbelievable.
They didn't know who the woman was
let alone who had done it
and I sat there and said
poor woman
hope they get the bloke
and he stared at the wall
just above the telly.
I noticed it as I looked round.
What's up?
I said.
No answer.
Not worried about money again, are you?
Yep, he said.
So I said a bit how maybe we shouldn't go out so often
and running a nice car like that takes quite a bit out of
    your pocket
and that was that.

Again next day
I found myself thinking about it.
Him staring at the wall.
And that was my first panic attack.
I don't know what it was
but I suddenly felt as if I didn't know him.

I was lying in bed with him,
we were getting as close as it's possible for two people
    to be –
I mean when you have sex
you give yourself up, don't you?
You can't be going at it with all you've got
thinking, this bloke makes me sick
he disgusts me.
You've got to trust
he's not going to do you any harm
and I did.
I did trust him
I liked him
but suddenly I came over cold
thinking
I do not know him
he is a blank page.
We've been going out all this time and
I just don't know him
he could be anybody
he could be Frankenstein in his private life
for all I knew.

Next time I was with him
I suddenly began to find him a bit creepy.
He just seemed to be going through the motions all the
    time.
He didn't seem to be someone doing things
because he wanted to be doing things,
it was like he just did them
because that was what people did.
I can't put my finger on it exactly
it was just that everything he did –
like go over and get a cup of tea
or sit down on a chair –
he did it all very neatly
very precisely

but like he was just doing what he was told
he wasn't doing it because he wanted to.
He didn't say,
what I could do with now
is a nice cup of tea
and then sit there swilling tea down his throat,
he did it all quietly
and neatly and without any go in him.
He didn't have any lust about him.
I suddenly found him very very creepy.
When he walked
I noticed all of a sudden
that he didn't move his hips.
From his neck down to his knees
it was as if it was all in plaster
he was like a robot.
You could believe he was real
but he was actually a robot.
It was then I realised
that's how he was in bed.
He was just doing it because he had been told
that's what you do
and he was doing as he was told.

Of course, all this was rubbish.
I'm not saying it really was like this
it was just that that was the way it felt to me.
But then
for all I knew he was an alien.
I had never asked him,
Are you an alien?
I had scarcely ever asked him anything.
I was looking at a stranger
I had been going out with
for ages.
How could I have done it?
How could I have wanted him so much?

How could I have got so randy with him?
And now suddenly feel he was such a creep?

When the police came for him
I was so wrapped up with myself
I hardly noticed it.
I was still in this panic
of wondering how could I be the kind of person
that could have got with the kind of person
who I now thought was such a creep?
I was in a panic with myself.
Worse than not knowing who he was
I didn't know who I was.
Into all that came two policemen
and out of it went two policemen and the bloke.

You know the rest.

I know too much now. There's things I didn't want to know
but I know them now. And what am I supposed to do with it
all?

I sit here knowing things but if someone else looks at me I
look like I know nothing. I've seen my face in the mirror and
it looks like I know nothing. But I know loads and I don't know
what to do with it.

I don't know what to do with the tapes either.